Peedie Bee

by Michelle Robertson

Peedie Bee, our fuzzy flying friend

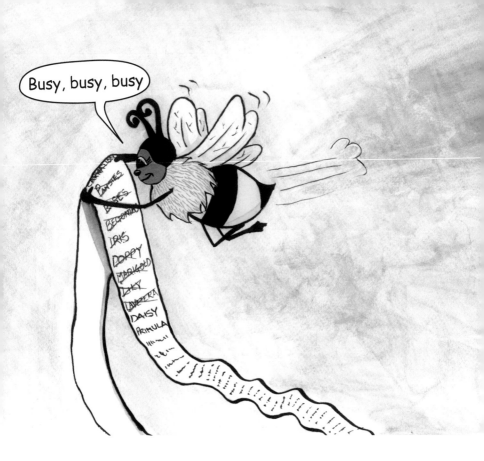

Whose working day just has no end

She buzzes around for hours and hours

Kissing the plants and hugging the flowers

She works for love and not for money

Making such beautiful golden honey

Fine wax and royal jelly, too

or her Queen and babies, for me and for you

With no Peedie Bee the flowers we cherish

Would wither away and slowly perish

Please, don't chase her away,
give her a chance

She's not angry or mad,
she just loves to dance

Next time you meet, tell her she's great

She's the one who puts honey on your plate

Peedie helps keep all the flowers alive

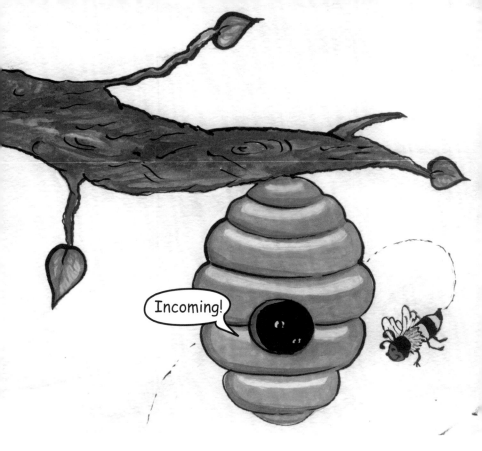

nd builds honeycombs in her marvellous hive

Thank you, Peedie Bee, for all that you do

Our planet thinks the world of you!

ISBN 978-1-902957-44-9

Printed and Published
by The Orcadian
Hatston
Kirkwall
Orkney
KW15 1DW

www.orcadian.co.uk